THE WORLD'S MOST MOVING MUSIC

ARRANGED FOR SOLO PIANO

PUBLISHED BY:
WISE PUBLICATIONS,
8/9 FRITH STREET, LONDON W1D 3JB, ENGLAND.

EXCLUSIVE DISTRIBUTORS:
MUSIC SALES LIMITED,
DISTRIBUTION CENTRE, NEWMARKET ROAD, BURY ST EDMUNDS, SUFFOLK IP33 3YB, ENGLAND.
MUSIC SALES PTY LIMITED,
120 ROTHSCHILD AVENUE, ROSEBERY, NSW 2018, AUSTRALIA.

ORDER NO. AM982520
ISBN 1-84449-996-0
THIS BOOK © COPYRIGHT 2005 WISE PUBLICATIONS,
A DIVISION OF MUSIC SALES LIMITED.

ARRANGING AND ENGRAVING SUPPLIED BY CAMDEN MUSIC.

PRINTED IN THE UNITED KINGDOM.

YOUR GUARANTEE OF QUALITY:
AS PUBLISHERS, WE STRIVE TO PRODUCE EVERY BOOK TO THE HIGHEST COMMERCIAL STANDARDS.
THE MUSIC HAS BEEN FRESHLY ENGRAVED AND CAREFULLY DESIGNED TO MINIMISE
AWKWARD PAGE TURNS TO MAKE PLAYING FROM IT A REAL PLEASURE.
PARTICULAR CARE HAS BEEN GIVEN TO SPECIFYING ACID-FREE, NEUTRAL-SIZED
PAPER MADE FROM PULPS WHICH HAVE NOT BEEN ELEMENTAL CHLORINE BLEACHED.
THIS PULP IS FROM FARMED SUSTAINABLE FORESTS AND WAS PRODUCED
WITH SPECIAL REGARD FOR THE ENVIRONMENT.
THROUGHOUT, THE PRINTING AND BINDING HAVE BEEN PLANNED TO ENSURE A STURDY,
ATTRACTIVE PUBLICATION WHICH SHOULD GIVE YEARS OF ENJOYMENT.
IF YOUR COPY FAILS TO MEET OUR HIGH STANDARDS, PLEASE INFORM US AND WE WILL GLADLY REPLACE IT.

WWW.MUSICSALES.COM

THIS PUBLICATION IS NOT AUTHORISED FOR SALE IN
THE UNITED STATES OF AMERICA AND/OR CANADA.

WISE PUBLICATIONS
PART OF THE MUSIC SALES GROUP
LONDON/NEW YORK/PARIS/SYDNEY/COPENHAGEN/BERLIN/MADRID/TOKYO

ABIDE WITH ME
(FROM 'EVENTIDE')
WILLIAM HENRY MONK
PAGE 8

ADAGIO FOR STRINGS
(FEATURED IN THE FILM 'PLATOON')
SAMUEL BARBER
PAGE 4

ADAGIO IN G MINOR
(FEATURED IN THE FILM 'GALLIPOLI')
TOMASO ALBINONI
PAGE 9

AGNUS DEI
(FROM 'REQUIEM')
GABRIEL FAURÉ
PAGE 14

AVE MARIA
JOHANN SEBASTIAN BACH /
CHARLES GOUNOD
PAGE 18

AVE VERUM CORPUS
WILLIAM BYRD
PAGE 22

AVE VERUM CORPUS
WOLFGANG AMADEUS MOZART
PAGE 24

BALCONY SCENE
(FEATURED IN THE FILM 'WILLIAM SHAKESPEARE'S ROMEO AND JULIET')
CRAIG ARMSTRONG / MARIUS DE VRIES / NELLEE HOOPER
PAGE 26

CRUCIFIXUS
(FROM 'MASS IN B MINOR')
JOHANN SEBASTIAN BACH
PAGE 30

THE DEAD MARCH
(FROM 'SAUL')
GEORGE FRIDERIC HANDEL
PAGE 38

DIES IRAE
(FROM 'REQUIEM')
GIUSEPPE VERDI
PAGE 40

FUNERAL MARCH
(FROM 'PIANO SONATA NO.2 IN B♭ MINOR')
FRÉDÉRIC CHOPIN
PAGE 33

IN PARADISUM
(FROM 'REQUIEM' AND FEATURED IN THE FILM 'THE THIN RED LINE')
GABRIEL FAURÉ
PAGE 44

LACHRIMAE ANTIQUAE
(FLOW MY TEARS)
JOHN DOWLAND
PAGE 50

LACRIMOSA
(FROM 'REQUIEM IN D MINOR' AND FEATURED IN THE FILM 'AMADEUS')
WOLFGANG AMADEUS MOZART
PAGE 52

THE LAMB
(FEATURED IN THE 'ORANGE' TV ADVERT)
JOHN TAVENER
PAGE 54

LASCIA CH'IO PIANGA
(FROM 'RINALDO')
GEORGE FRIDERIC HANDEL
PAGE 47

NIMROD
(FROM 'ENIGMA' VARIATIONS AND
FEATURED IN THE FILM 'ELIZABETH')
EDWARD ELGAR
PAGE 56

NOCTURNE IN C♯ MINOR
(FEATURED IN THE FILM 'THE PIANIST')
FRÉDÉRIC CHOPIN
PAGE 58

PANIS ANGELICUS
CÉSAR FRANCK
PAGE 70

PAVANE POUR UNE INFANTE DÉFUNTE
MAURICE RAVEL
PAGE 62

PIE JESU
(FROM 'REQUIEM')
ANDREW LLOYD WEBBER
PAGE 68

REQUIEM AETERNAM
(FROM 'REQUIEM IN D MINOR'
AND FEATURED IN THE FILM 'AMADEUS')
WOLFGANG AMADEUS MOZART
PAGE 73

SARABANDE
(FEATURED IN THE 'LEVI'S JEANS' TV ADVERT)
GEORGE FRIDERIC HANDEL
PAGE 76

SCHINDLER'S LIST THEME
(FEATURED IN THE FILM 'SCHINDLER'S LIST')
JOHN WILLIAMS
PAGE 78

SIX FEET UNDER
(FEATURED IN THE TV SERIES 'SIX FEET UNDER')
THOMAS NEWMAN
PAGE 82

SOLEMN MELODY
WALFORD DAVIES
PAGE 84

STABAT MATER
GIOVANNI BATTISTA PERGOLESI
PAGE 87

SYMPHONY NO.5 IN C♯ MINOR
(4TH MOVEMENT: ADAGIETTO
AND FEATURED IN THE FILM 'DEATH IN VENICE')
GUSTAV MAHLER
PAGE 90

THOU KNOWEST, LORD
(FUNERAL MUSIC FOR QUEEN MARY)
HENRY PURCELL
PAGE 92

WHEN I AM LAID IN EARTH
(FROM 'DIDO AND AENEAS')
HENRY PURCELL
PAGE 94

Adagio for Strings
(featured in the film *Platoon*)

Composed by Samuel Barber

Arranged by Jack Long

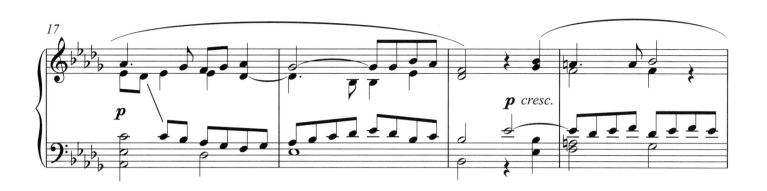

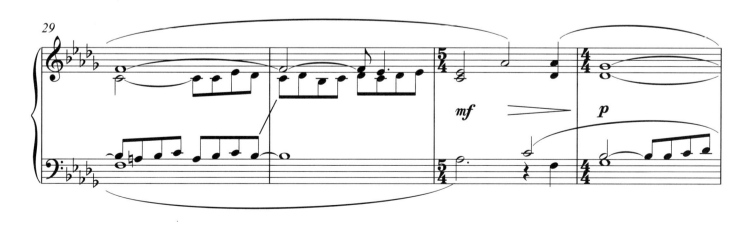

(with increasing intensity)

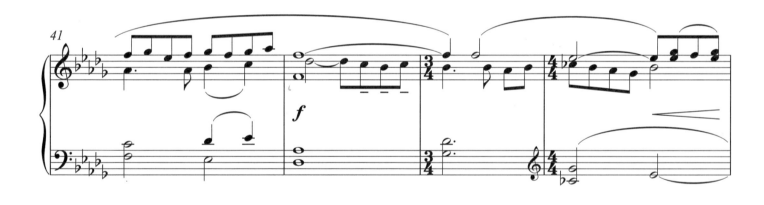

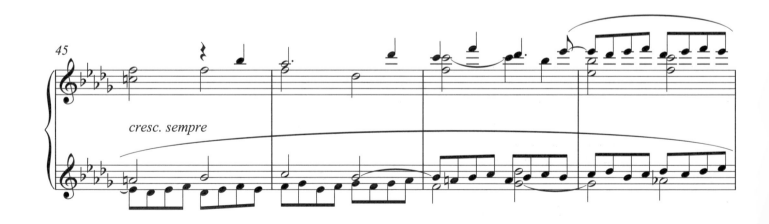

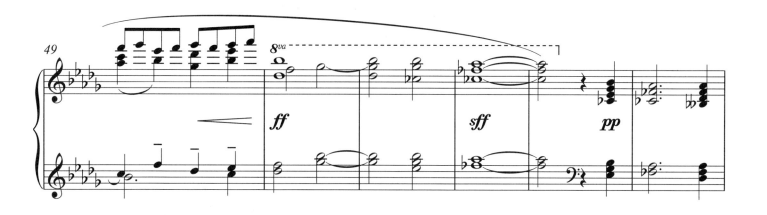

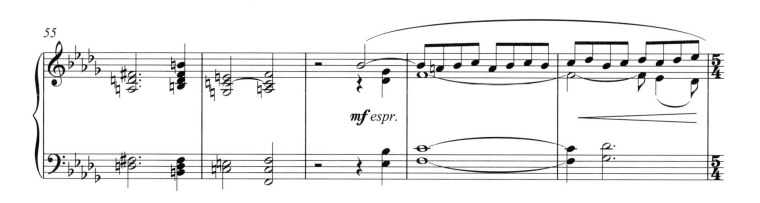

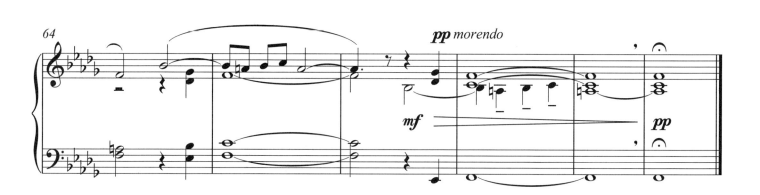

Abide With Me
(from Eventide)

Composed by William Henry Monk
Arranged by Quentin Thomas

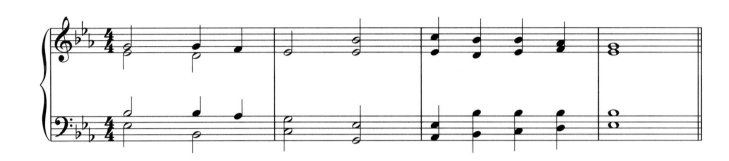

Adagio in G minor

(featured in the film *Gallipoli*)

Composed by Tomaso Albinoni, realised by Remo Giazotto
Arranged by Jack Long

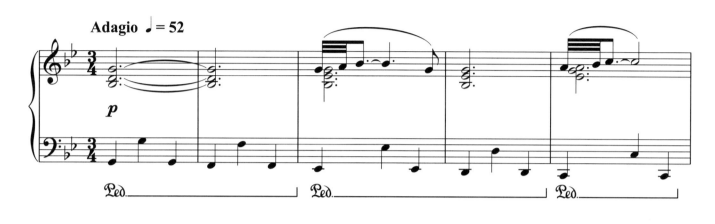

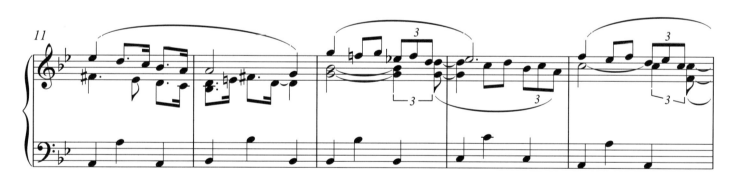

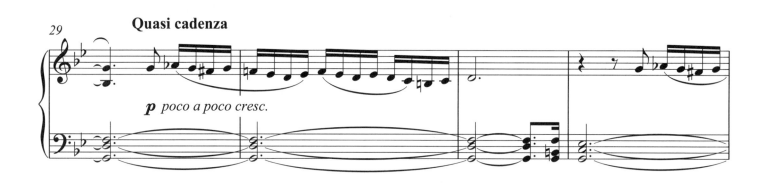

Quasi cadenza

Agnus Dei
(from Requiem)

Composed by Gabriel Fauré

Ave Maria
(Based on Johann Sebastian Bach's Prelude No.1 in C major)

Composed by Charles Gounod

Ave Verum Corpus

Composed by William Byrd

Arranged by Quentin Thomas

Ave Verum Corpus

Composed by Wolfgang Amadeus Mozart

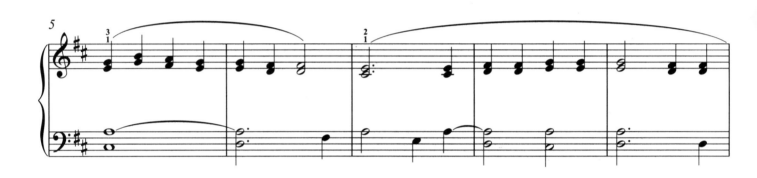

Balcony Scene

(from the film *William Shakespeare's Romeo and Juliet*)

Words and Music by Craig Armstrong, Paul Hooper and Marius De Vries

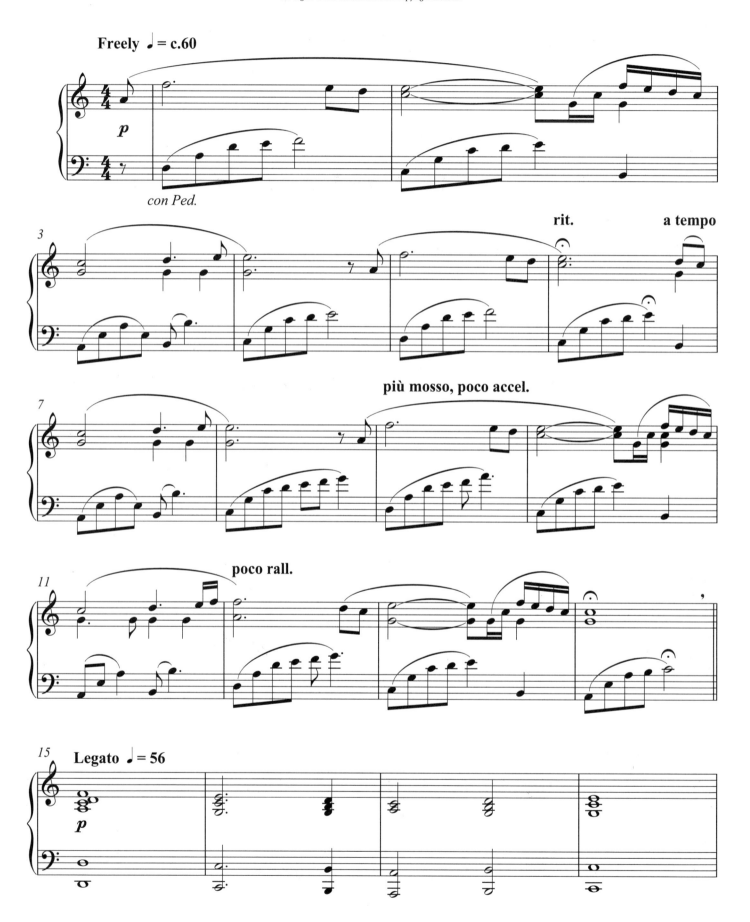

Crucifixus
(from Mass in B minor)

Composed by Johann Sebastian Bach

Arranged by Quentin Thomas

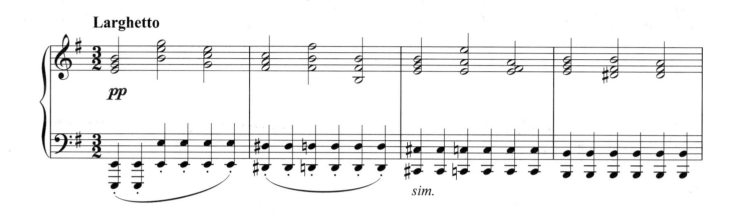

Funeral March
(from Piano Sonata No.2 in B♭ minor)

Composed by Frédéric Chopin

cresc. poco a poco

The Dead March
(from Saul)

Composed by George Frideric Handel

Dies Irae
(from Requiem)

Composed by Giuseppe Verdi

Arranged by Quentin Thomas

Allegro agitato (♩ = 80)

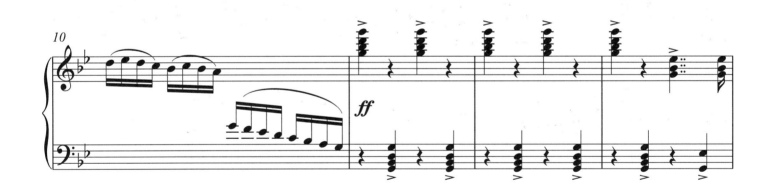

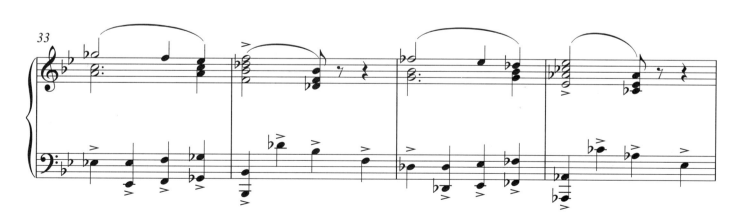

In Paradisum

(from Requiem and featured in the film *The Thin Red Line*)

Composed by Gabriel Fauré

Arranged by Quentin Thomas

Lascia Ch'io Pianga
(from Rinaldo)

Composed by George Frideric Handel

Lachrimae Antiquae (Flow My Tears)

Composed by John Dowland

Arranged by Jerry Lanning

Slowly ♩ = 64

Lacrimosa

(from Requiem in D minor and featured in the film *Amadeus*)

Composed by Wolfgang Amadeus Mozart

The Lamb

(featured in the *Orange* TV advert)

Words by William Blake and Music by John Tavener

Arranged by Jerry Lanning

Nimrod
(from 'Enigma' Variations and featured in the film *Elizabeth*)

Composed by Edward Elgar

Nocturne in C♯ minor, Op. Posth.

(featured in the film *The Pianist*)

Composed by Frédéric Chopin

Arranged by Jerry Lanning

Lento con gran espressione ♩ = 68

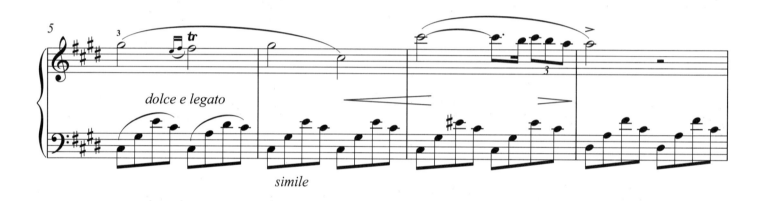

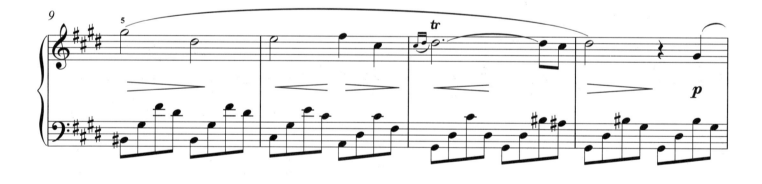

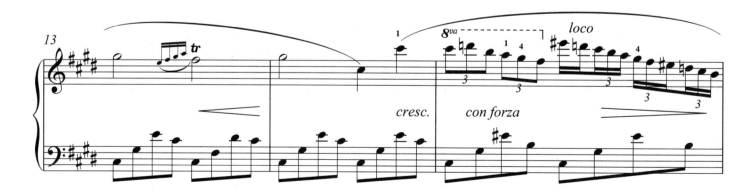

Pavane Pour Une Infante Défunte

Composed by Maurice Ravel

Assez doux, mais d'une sonorité large ($\quad$ = 54)

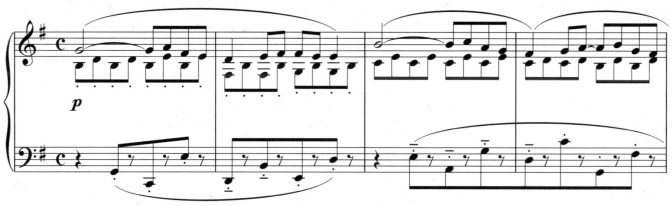

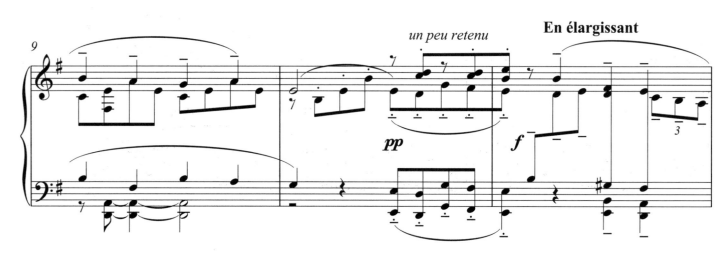

1er Mouvt.   Très lointain

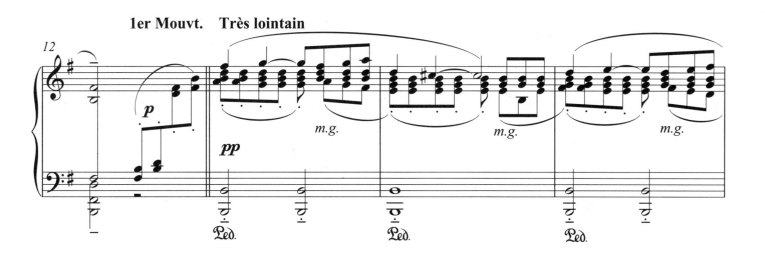

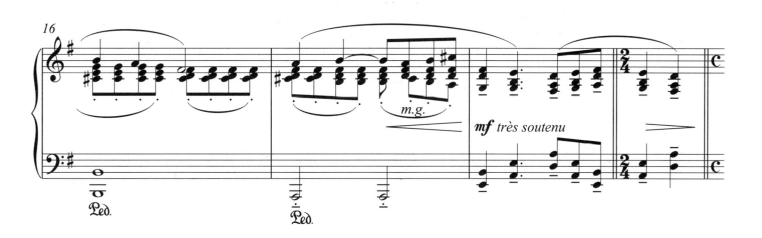

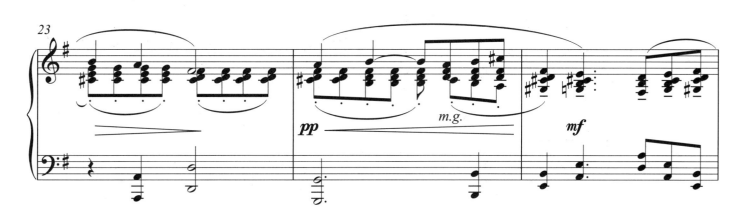

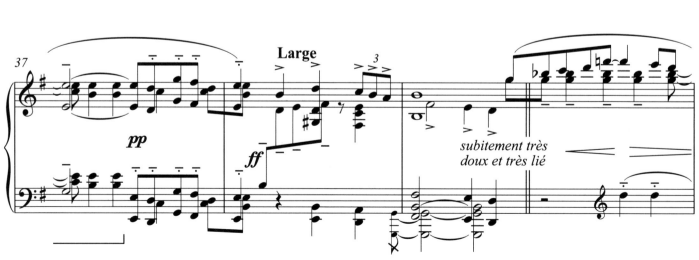

Cédez

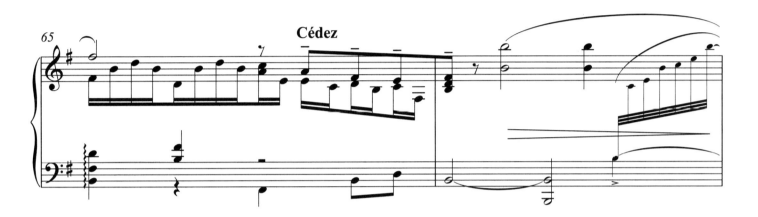

Reprenez le mouvement

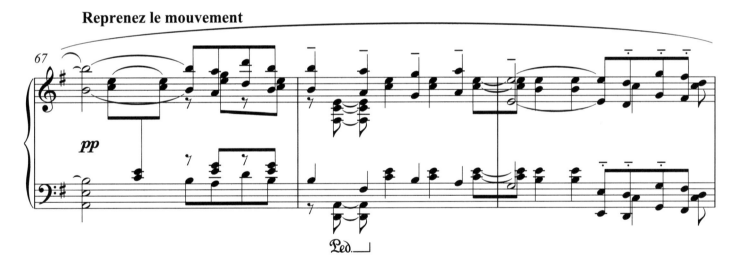

En élargissant beaucoup

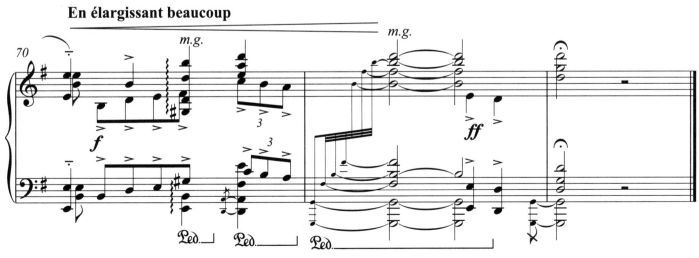

Pie Jesu
(from Requiem)

Composed by Andrew Lloyd Webber

Arranged by Quentin Thomas

Andante

Panis Angelicus

Composed by César Franck

Arranged by Quentin Thomas

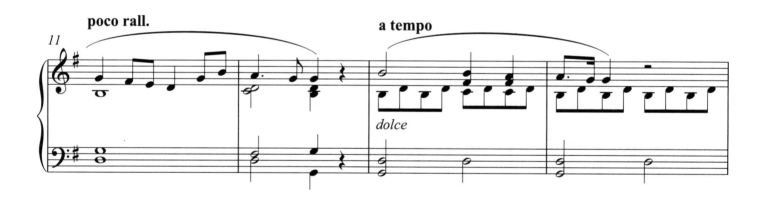

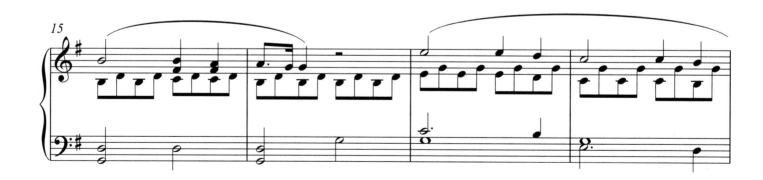

Requiem Aeternam

(from Requiem in D minor and featured in the film *Amadeus*)

Composed by Wolfgang Amadeus Mozart

Arranged by Quentin Thomas

Sarabande

(featured in the *Levi's Jeans* TV advert)

Composed by George Frideric Handel

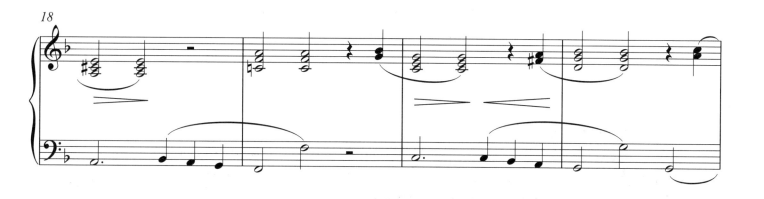

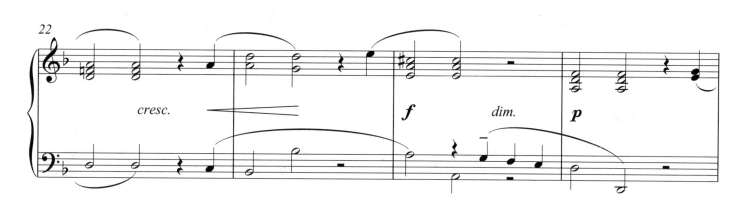

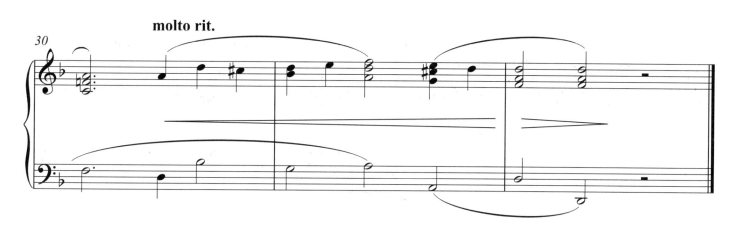

Schindler's List Theme

(from the film *Schindler's List*)

Composed by John Williams

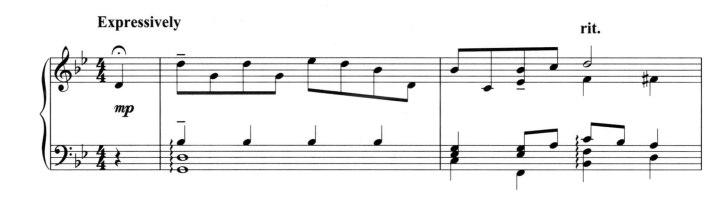

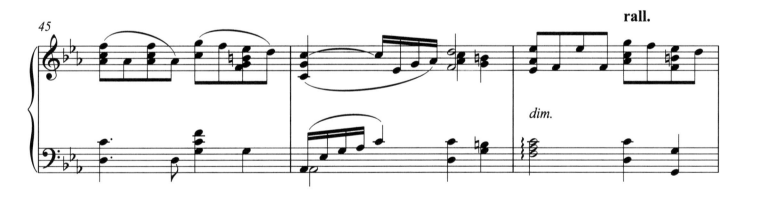

Six Feet Under

(from the TV series *Six Feet Under*)

Composed by Thomas Newman

Moderately fast ♩ = 112

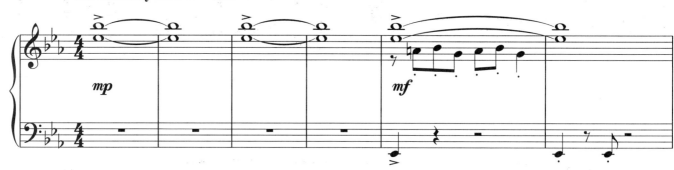

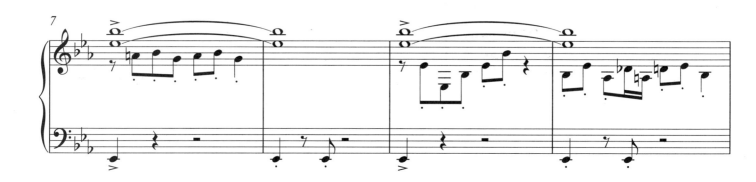

Solemn Melody

Composed by Henry Walford Davies

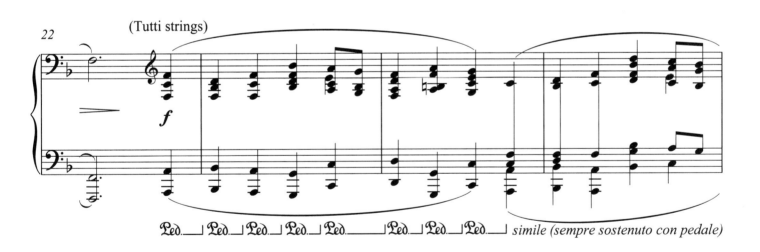

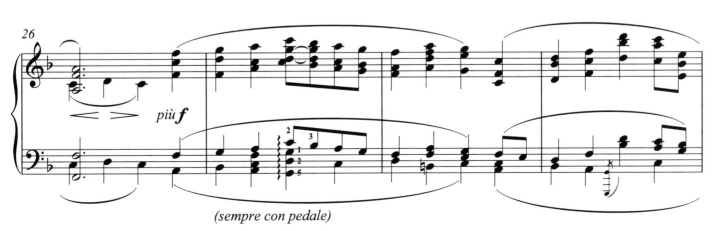

Stabat Mater

Composed by Giovanni Battista Pergolesi

Arranged by Quentin Thomas

Symphony No.5 in C♯ minor

(4th movement: Adagietto, featured in the film *Death In Venice*)

Composed by Gustav Mahler

Thou Knowest, Lord

(Funeral Music for Queen Mary, featured in the funeral service of Princess Diana)

Composed by Henry Purcell

Arranged by Quentin Thomas

Slow

93

When I Am Laid In Earth

(from Dido and Aeneas)

Composed by Henry Purcell

Arranged by Quentin Thomas

123456789